To the memory of my deceased parents

Teresa and Edward Fogarty

Acknowledgements

Many thanks to Maria Ward for her editorial work on this book.

About the Author

Patricia Fogarty has spent much of her adult life working as a teacher and in her spare time enjoys writing. In 2015, she produced a collection of essays entitled *Tales from Memory Lane in Palmerstown* for the Palmerstown Festival. To mark both the occasions of the centenary of the 1916 Rising and the Palmerstown Festival, she has written the novella *Ettie's Road to the Rising*. She lives in Palmerstown with her husband and two adult children.

Chapter 1

Needless to say, I have no recollection of my birth other than to say I was born on the 4th of January 1870 to the Right Honourable Richard and Sybil Duckworth of Duckworth Grove in the Barony of Alm in the County of Roscommon.

But of course I should tell you that my great-grandfather, Thomas Duckworth, a Member of the Irish Parliament, had given tremendous support to the British colonial campaign and was handsomely rewarded with both land and money for his efforts, thus, enabling him to commission the building of the Grove. The Grove itself was constructed from granite stone and designed in a neo-Palladian style similar to many of the other grand houses dotted here and there on the Irish landscape around that time. Our estate, Duckworth Grove, consisted of approximately twelve thousand acres and these lands stretched into the neighbouring County of Galway.

There was a considerably large age-gap between myself and my only sibling, William. By the time I was four years old, he was already reading Law in Cambridge, after having been to boarding school in Surrey for what seemed like an incredibly long time. William was the heir to Duckworth Grove and according to our servants his birth was greeted with great rejoicing by Papa. According to our servants too, he was absolutely elated when Mama gave birth to me.

Papa loathed many of the social pursuits expected of our social class that entailed cruelty in any form to God's creatures. His feelings about it were so strong that he absolutely forbade members of the nearby Hunt to encroach on our land during the fox-hunting season. In fact, any time a ball was staged at the Grove, Papa, used the opportunity to condemn cruelty of any sort and chose instead to speak at length on the subject of his large collection of exotic plants and trees which flourished in the gardens and woodland of our home. Papa had little interest in politics unlike his older brother, Thomas, who was a member of the House of Lords. The only exception to this occurred when his school friend, Charles Stewart Parnell, was a guest of Mama and Papa at the Grove.

I spent the first five years of my life mainly in the nursery and in the company of my nanny, Ellen Browne. Ellen, or Ellie as I called her, was a very caring and gentle woman and I loved her dearly. On fine days she used to bring me out into the fresh air in my perambulator and wheel me about our estate. When I became a little older and could walk a sizeable distance, I held Ellie's hand as we went on our little ramble.

On one of our frequent rambles, Ellie brought me to meet some of the peasant children that lived on our estate. I remember it so, so well when Ellie introduced them to me. Ellie walked me up to an open door of a tiny little cottage and, as we approached it, lots of little children similar in age to me came running to greet us. Their clothes were very different from mine and they were barefooted. They all clamoured around Ellie and me and spoke excitedly in an odd language. I thought they were a strange lot. Yet, they were so friendly, as they kept looking at me and smiling. I was frightened, and as Ellie and I entered through the doorway of this place, I clung tightly to her.

Inside there was a woman and, from what I can remember, she was very happy to see Ellie and me. Ellie handed her a basket of food and she seemed to have been delighted about this. She and Ellie spoke for a while and then we left this dark little place. Ellie waved to them and we made our journey home.

That night, as Ellie dressed me for bed, I asked her about the odd people whom we had met that day. I cannot remember what Ellie told me about them. But I still remember clearly their strange clothes, bare feet and the peculiar way they spoke. I had never heard such odd sounds before then and I liked them. Our servants spoke differently from Mama and Papa. But these people sounded stranger still. Some years later I learned that they had been speaking a different language; it was Gaelic mixed with English.

Around the same time too, I had become a 'big girl' as I was allowed to join Mama and Papa for dinner in the evening in the main dining room of the Grove. As young as I was, I had mixed feelings about this affair as I had to 'behave myself' and was expected to hold enormous knives and forks in a peculiar way. According to Papa, more often than not, however, and to my parents' amusement, I paid little or no attention to either the cumbersome cutlery or the food. Instead, I created rather a din as I played with my toy spinner at the dining room table.

Some evenings I could still have my dinner with Ellie, in the nursery. That occurred when Mama was feeling unwell and Papa was far away in Dublin or London at some botanical exhibition. However, once Papa returned I had to resume eating in the dining room in the evening. More and more, Papa and I ate without Mama's company at the table, as Mama had become very unwell. I can remember so clearly Papa's sad face as he rarely laughed at my silly pranks.

Sometimes Ellie brought me to visit Mama in her bedroom. I remember those occasions clearly as Mama was always so gentle and kind to me and would hold me in her arms and say 'Ettie, always be gentle, always be kind to all'. I didn't fully understand what Mama was saying at that time. However, the phrase remained with me and years later that sentiment was to almost become my mantra.

Time moved on. Mama seemed to have been unwell for a very long time and during the Winter of 1876 she died. Although I was then six years old I didn't understand at the time that Mama would never be returning to Duckworth Grove. To my child's mind it seemed perfectly rational that 'If you can go to Heaven, there's no reason why you can't come back from it'.

William came home from Cambridge to attend Mama's funeral. I had not seen him for such a long time. The age-gap between William and I, was one of almost twelve years. Years later, I learned that Mama had had two stillbirths in the intervening years between William's birth and my own. I really loved my big gentle brother and I loved him even more as he had arrived home for Mama's funeral with a most wondrous gift, for me, a spaniel puppy. I called him Floss. He was a Welsh Spaniel. Floss rarely left my side and sadly died of old age when I was seventeen years old. I loved that dog and often felt that he was more perceptive than the adults around me. The arrival of Floss eased in a little way the pain of Mama's departure.

It was around that time too that Mildred Foster arrived into my life. Why I say 'arrived' is because she had to have been the most colourful and flamboyant person I'd ever met up to then. William was still home at the time and I can only guess that he had played a major part in Papa's recruitment of her as my governess. She was from the County of Cavan, had been educated in Dublin Town and had spent some time in Paris as a governess. She was employed by Papa to teach me English and Piano. After a couple of years, her role as my governess expanded to incorporate into my tuition the additional subjects of Mathematics,

French, History and Needlepoint, plus all matters concerning etiquette that would be required of me as a future society debutante in London. Papa was a little perplexed by Mildred as he soon discovered her to be one of the most unconventional individuals he had ever encountered.

Years later, I found out that Mildred and William moved in the same circle in London. Her apparel alone was a little odd to say the least and, in addition to that, she often arrived into the nursery classroom wearing an outlandish hat that she had designed and made herself. Generally, class began with a prayer followed by Mildred singing the hymn *Abide with Me* and I sang along with her when I was older, in spite of being desperately out of tune! She seems to have made it her business to become friendly with all of the people that lived on Papa's estate and she told me that 'All people are equal in the eyes of God'.

Soon after Mama's funeral, William returned to University and after graduating he went directly to South Africa to work as a barrister. Papa was bitterly disappointed by this, as he felt William should have returned home to help with managing the estate to which was heir. In truth, Papa had little interest in running the estate and had dearly wished that William had. He was saddened too to learn of the attitude that some of his Society friends had towards William. Apparently, William was making a name for himself in South Africa as a campaigner for social justice for the poor and, to make matters worse, to Papa's utter dismay, he was living in a shack of some sort there. William, it would seem, had totally distanced himself from our way of life.

In 1878, William came home from South Africa on a visit. I remember it as if it was only yesterday. Prior to his arrival, he had sent a telegram to say that he had disembarked safely in Dublin, that he had a few people to meet and matters to attend to there and, when he would have had those 'matters' done, he'd be with us in a day or two. As young as I was, I was curious to know what those 'matters' were. I asked Ellie what did she think about those 'matters' as I'd convinced myself that those 'matters' had to have been William's acquisition in Dublin of another puppy for Floss and myself. To my surprise Ellie was displeased about the 'matters' and requested me to not mention them again. Needless to say all this 'matters' business added to my excitement regarding William's arrival, he, the big brother that made me laugh and whom I remembered even making me laugh at darling Mama's funeral although I was so sad.

Finally, William arrived home and he brought with him for me not a puppy but a big soft doll. I had to content myself with her and not another puppy so I called her Matters. I cannot recall much else regarding William's visit. However, I do remember well a horrid argument that took place between Papa and William one morning at breakfast-time. Ellie told me that my brother had strange ideas but that did not make me any the wiser as I did not know what 'strange ideas' were. Later, I was to learn that William was following both Irish Republican and Socialist ideas and that he was very actively trying to apply his socialist ideals in the Transvaal in South Africa. It seems that William had already embraced the idea of social reform and that of the Chartist Movement whilst he was still in Cambridge.

I never saw William again, because three years later he was killed in cross-fire during one of the skirmishes that followed the First Boer War. Sadly, Papa never learned the full details of his only son's death.

During his lifetime, William had made a name for himself as a campaigner for social justice in South Africa though some of the British newspapers of the time were highly critical of him and, indeed, within society circles, both in England and Ireland, there were many people who condemned him. In fact, one particular newspaper after his death printed a most un-kind editorial castigating William and branded him as 'An aristocratic disgrace to the Empire'.

His fall from grace among the Irish Ascendancy was highly evident, as many of our social contemporaries declined to attend his memorial service at our church which was situated just outside the main gates of the Grove.

William had truly, as the saying goes, 'broken the mould', as not only had he rejected the value system of his own social class but, he had taken it a step further and rejected the idea that black people were in any way inferior to the white man.

Of course, at eleven years of age, William's way of life in South Africa meant little or nothing to me. I was far too young to understand what it was all about. All I knew at the time was that I had lost my big, kind and gentle brother and that he too was gone to Heaven to be with Mama and, as great a place as Heaven was, Heaven did not let people get out of it.

After William's death, Papa withdrew more and more from everyday life and he spent most of his days indoors in the library, reading his geographic and botany journals, preferring not to be disturbed. He had become a virtual recluse shunning any form of social entertainment. Papa, who had once been so jolly and outgoing to all, had become like a shadow of his former self. It pained me to see him so. However, he seemed to find some form of solace caring for nature's beautiful flowers and plants. Yet, this was a solitary past-time.

Of course, I ignored Papa's desire for solitude and I was extremely curious to know what else held his interest for those long hours that he engrossed himself in the library reading. Eventually, I was able to determine that the subject of his focus was the Bible and that he had developed a profound interest in perusing the Gospels therein.

Papa and I now attended Church Service regularly. I loved our outings to our local church. I paid little or no attention to what our Vicar was preaching from the pulpit. Our pew was at the very front of the church and I found it very boring to sit still. So I entertained myself looking around at the people behind me.

Our Vicar, Reverend Simon Whyte, and my Papa had become friends and sometimes he paid a visit to our home for afternoon tea. Papa thoroughly enjoyed his company and they often spent hours in the library engaged in deep discussion. On such occasions instead of his usual woebegone face, Papa looked relatively happy.

Papa was leaving even more of the management of the estate to a man called Thomas. Thomas was from the neighbouring County of Galway and he managed the estate as best as he could at the time. Why I say this, is because the whole Irish Land Question was dominating Irish political and social affairs.

Again, I was far too young to understand the complexities of the Irish Land Question and Ellie, who was oblivious to the entire agrarian unrest in Ireland, was unable to enlighten me. She had a very simplistic outlook on life and she never felt the need to question the *status quo*. She went from day to day, secure in the knowledge that when the time came for her to retire from service she could live out her old-age in comfort at the Grove in the servant's quarters.

I was really fond of Ellie as she provided me with a sense of security and she had a lovely motherly way about her. Later on when her role as a nanny to me was no longer required, she became my companion. When I was home from boarding school, it was she who listened to my stories.

Unlike Ellie, Mildred, my governess, seemed to have made it her business to be keenly aware of the situation pertaining to the Irish Land Question. She often requested free evenings from Papa, telling him that she had some social calls to make. I do not think that Papa cared too much where she was or what she did. She seemed to have been absorbed in the whole 'land war' issue, into which the Irish Land Question had materialised in the County of Mayo.

In her wisdom, Mildred felt it was her moral duty as my governess to tell me about the social unrest that was occurring in the neighbouring County between the landlords and their tenants. Of course, her stories were most unpleasant. She told me that tenants could be evicted from their cottages at any time by their landlord and that many of them lived in poverty throughout the County of Mayo and indeed, the County of Roscommon too. She spoke about tenants setting fire to crops and maiming cattle as their way of protesting against having to pay unjust rents to their landlords. As young as I was, I knew we had a lot of land and that we too had tenants on our estate. It was all quite frightening. So I thought it best to put it to the back of my mind.

When I was very young, Ellie did not seem to mind me playing on an odd occasion with our tenant children. But, by the time I was nine or ten years old she felt it would not be appropriate for me to have any interaction with 'them' as she said 'I was a young lady and they were mere 'peasants' or 'bumpkins'. I remember thinking at the time that she had funny ideas and it seemed to me too, that lots of people had 'strange ideas'. I also thought too, that grown-ups had very odd words and phrases that meant little or nothing to me.

Maybe it was Mildred's influence upon Papa, coupled with his general despondency with life, which resulted in his subsequent decision to send me to a boarding school in the County of Dublin for my continued education. Mildred held a firm belief that women should have an education equal to any man. Formal education for Mama and her social contemporaries rarely went beyond that taught by the family governess of the house in question. The prospect of going to a strange place with strange people whom I did not know both scared and excited me at the same time. I dreaded the thoughts of being parted from the people I knew and worse again, I would only see Floss at holiday time.

Mildred did not do anything to help allay my fears regarding the prospect of boarding school or, indeed, any other matter. She was convinced that the day would come soon when Ireland's ascendancy class would no longer dominate Irish society and she firmly believed that the Irish peasants would and should own their own patch of a few acres.

All this was a lot for me to try to understand and it did not make much sense to me. I was still too young to grapple with the whole concept of social justice and, as far as I was concerned, the tenants on Papa's estate seemed to be happy with their lot and the ones that were not, left and went to England or America.

Nevertheless, it must have played on my mind as I approached Papa after dinner in the library one evening not long after Mildred had spoken to me about it. To my amazement, Papa's views concurred with Mildred's opinions and he told me that 'Our days are almost numbered, as men like Parnell and Davitt are implementing changes to land ownership in Ireland which would have a profound effect on our life-style'.

It all sounded terribly odd and, as far as I was concerned, Duckworth Grove would never change. So, Mildred and Papa had to have been speaking nonsense. I mean, to where can twelve thousand acres disappear and given that the Grove itself was built from granite stone how could that building vanish? Silly grown-ups! After all, Charles Stewart Parnell knew Mama and Papa and he had been in College with Papa so why would he possibly want to make our home disappear? Mildred even said that Charles and another man called Michael Davitt had been in the County of Mayo encouraging tenants to withhold their rents from their landlords as part of his role as President of the Irish Land League. It all sounded so complicated and I felt that the best thing I could do was forget about it and that did not take me too long!

In the Summer of 1881, the year William was killed, my cousin, Harold, and his sister Georgina came to stay for a fortnight at the Grove. Harold and Georgina were my late mother's nephew and niece and their home was Tudorham House in the County of Down. Harold was two years older than I and he was such great fun. Georgina was less than a year older than I.

Their parents, my Aunt Edith and her husband, my Uncle Arthur, seemed to have little or no control over their off-spring and from what Georgina told me, it seemed that governesses did not stay too long at Tudorham House. She hated them all. Uncle Arthur was a military and diplomatic man and had spent much of his time in Burma and India, whilst my Aunt Edith ran Tudorham House. I remember her as a very strict lady and, as strict as she was, it had little impact on Harold and, for that matter, on Georgina.

Georgina was a proper bookworm and she spent most of her time at the Grove reading especially when she was not making rude faces at everyone. It seemed that she was almost born with a contempt for any form of etiquette or good manners. She frequently shouted at Ellie and at our other servants in a most rude manner. Dare Ellie request her to retire to bed, she would scream obscenities at her.

Harold and I became great friends running wild and playing Blind Man's Bluff and Hunt the Thimble in the woodland of the Grove. He told me that when he'd grow up, he was going to become a military man just like his Papa.

Ellie by that stage, positively discouraged me from having any social interaction with the tenant children. However, as Harold and I spent many hours each day playing in the woodland, it was inevitable that we would encounter them sooner or later. Naturally, when Harold and I were in the woodland and well out of Ellie's sight, away from her disapproving glare, we took the opportunity to make friends with them. That chance came when we saw three of them playing with a ball of some sort nearby. I do not exactly remember how we began talking to them but, they seemed like a decent lot and it was not long until we were all running around together and laughing.

All too soon, their two week holiday was over and Harold and Georgina had to return to their home in the County of Down. Of course, I was sad to see them go and I hoped that they would return the following Summer.

I continued to play with the tenant children on our estate. Biddy was the eldest and I thought that she was so funny when she spoke as both her accent and her English were strange. I remember asking her to explain the meaning of the peculiar words - such as 'ag rith', 'ag gáire', 'ceart' - that she continuously used. With difficulty, she explained to me through English that these words were part of the Gaelic language, that Gaelic was the only language spoken at home and that school was the only place that she used English as all pupils, under law, were obliged to use English rather than Gaelic there. She was, however, very much aware that she would have to become good at English as she would most likely have to emigrate to England or far away to America, places where they only spoke English.

Though I had been accustomed to seeing them out and about on our estate and was familiar with their ill-fitting, drab and raggy clothes, I was not familiar with their language. I was so excited by the sound of this 'new language' that I begged Biddy to teach me some more of these words. That was my introduction to a whole new world linguistically, and in time culturally as well.

Biddy was a year older than I and she found the whole idea of teaching me Gaelic very strange. After all, in her mind, I was the daughter of the owner of the Big House. Regardless, I had become a regular pupil of Biddy and our classes were conducted in the woodland near the Grove. Biddy and I became good friends that Summer.

As you know, Ellie positively discouraged any social interaction between myself and the children of the estate. Without regard for Ellie's admonishments, I continued to play in the company of Biddy and her siblings for the remainder of the Summer of 1881.

Mildred left the Grove in September of that year and I was due to become a boarder at St. Andrew's Boarding School for Young Ladies in the County of Dublin. As a consequence I no longer required a governess. Mildred found a new position for herself in Dublin as a companion to Countess Hollington, who was well known in literary circles there.

My recollection of my departure to boarding school on the 11th of September 1881 remains vivid in my head to this day. Amid tears, I bid farewell to Papa and hugged him as I did when I was a little child. I remember his kindly smile and how he assured me that I woud love it there, at boarding school.

Ellie and I were taken to Dromod railway station in our horse-drawn carriage by O'Brien, our driver. I have to say I found it most difficult to conceal my excitement, as not only had I never rode in a railway train, I had never been to Dublin. For almost the entire journey I stared out the window and marvelled to myself as the changing landscape unfolded before me. Initially the land was boggy and stony. However, by the time we came to the County of Meath I saw fields the like of which I had never seen before. Those fields were large and lush green with well-kept fences and ditches. My mind flashed back to the contrasting poor land of the

County of Roscommon and I was almost overcome with a wave of homesickness. In my mind's eye, I saw Papa with my faithful Floss standing at the steps of the Grove as they did that morning waving me off. Already I missed them and Dash, my pony and I became more than slightly apprehensive about the prospect of living away from home.

Ellie sensed my apprehension and successfully distracted me with conversation. So much so, that my apprehension gave way to my mounting excitement as the train neared its destination. Its brakes screeched to a halt and our train-journey had ended: we had arrived at Broadstone railway station. My heart was thumping now with both fear and excitement as I stepped off the train onto the station platform. It was so crowded there as people jostled their way outside to the awaiting carriages.

Inside the station itself, a poorly clothed youth stood vending newspapers whilst an old woman sat on a stool of some sort selling apples from a basket which she held on her arm. There were beggars there too requesting alms. It was such a big noisy place the like of which I had never seen before and it stood in sharp contrast to sleepy Dromod railway station.

Outside the station, Ellie ordered a horse-drawn carriage to take both ourselves and my luggage to St. Andrew's Boarding School. A whole new world of Dublin Town spread before my eyes.

Our carriage driver drove in a southerly direction and crossed the dull grey River Liffey via Richmond Bridge and I smelled for the first time the strange smelling hops which wafted from the direction of the Guinness Brewery. We continued left along the quays towards Carlyle Bridge whereupon the driver made a right turn up Westmoreland Street where crowded trams passed us and people seemed to walk in every direction. We passed the entrance to Trinity College and we continued our journey directly south up Grafton Street which too was crowded with ladies and gents sporting the latest Parisian fashions. I was absolutely overawed by the sights, sounds and the aroma of coffee emanating from Bewley's Oriental Café on Grafton Street. We passed St. Stephen's Green and I must have fallen into a slumber as after that I have no recollection of the remainder of the journey. Ellie woke me just as our carriage had turned into the avenue to St. Andrew's, the school that was to become home to me for the following four years.

Chapter 2

A large group of parents, nannies and girls around my own age were gathered outside the main entrance of Saint Andrew's. With tears in my eyes, I bid Ellie adieu. Ellie returned to the awaiting driver and carriage. I felt totally forlorn as the carriage faded into the distance down the school driveway. The headmistress, Miss Baxter, summoned all us new girls to a roll-call and then we were shown to our respective dormitories by Miss Kent, who was also to become my form tutor. For the duration of my education in St. Andrew's, I shared a dormitory with Hanna Stynes-Wilson, Bessie Butler and Sybil Bruce.

Bessie's background was so different from my own. Yet, Bessie and I became close friends as we shared many of the same interests. However, one aspect of our friendship that both of us were really curious about was that of the Gaelic language though Bessie knew a lot more than I did about it. Her mother was employed from time to time as a monitor in the local national school in the County of Kilkenny. Not only did her mother possess a great interest in education, she also was a member of a voluntary group in the town of Kilkenny who met regularly to discuss Gaelic language and culture whilst her father was fully engaged in the management and day to day maintenance of their mixed farm.

Looking back to my early days of formal education with Mildred at the Grove, I realised then that, in her own unorthodox way, she had prepared me well for my continued education at St. Andrew's. Not only did we study English, Mathematics, French and History at St. Andrew's, the teachers there placed a large emphasis on our need to be both socially aware and at the same time be engaged in philanthropic work.

Fairly quickly, I settled into the school routine. However, there were times when I felt home-sick. But that feeling did not last too long as Bessie in her usual happy-go-lucky manner had me laughing at some silly event that had taken place earlier in the day. She had to have been one of the most outgoing characters I had ever met up to that point in my life. She was from a family of five siblings and from her accounts of them they were as boisterous as herself. I had yet to meet them. That opportunity came quicker than I anticipated. Our first half-term was over and we were given the opportunity to return to our respective homes for a week. Bessie insisted that I come with her to her family home in Kilkenny. As much as she insisted, I declined as I was so looking forward to seeing Papa and the rest of them at the Grove. Bessie was extremely disappointed so much so that without thinking I said I would visit her and her family during our Christmas break.

To my sheer delight at midterm, Papa came to collect me from St. Andrew's and, to add to the occasion, we travelled by tramway to Broadstone railway station and from there we continued by steam train to Dromod. As far as I can recollect I think I spoke non-stop to Papa for the duration of the journey. O'Brien, our driver, was waiting in the carriage for us at Dromod station and from there we made our way to the

Grove. I was overjoyed to see the familiar faces of the servants, Ellie and of course my darling dog, Floss!

After having supper with Papa on the evening of my return, I went over to the stables to see Dash. He was a friendly old dapple pony that originally was a gift from Mama and Papa to William and as William was no longer with us, he now belonged to me. Before I began boarding school I took him out for a trot in the paddock at the front of our home almost every day. Since I was away at school, the responsibility for exercising Dash fell to Peadar. Peadar was one of the stable-hands and although he was not too much older than I, he had a real fondness for all animals. He had more than kept his promise to me as Dash looked younger and better groomed than ever in his care.

Later that evening, I made my way over to the cottage that was home to Biddy and her family, the same little dark cottage that had frightened me so when I was a small child. Little or nothing had changed during my absence. Biddy was delighted to see me and the feeling was mutual. We talked and laughed just as we had done when we were younger. However, I was taken aback to learn that she was bound for America come early December of that year. Biddy's aunt had already left the village of Alm some years previously and had found work there as a lady's maid in Boston and Biddy was to work as a scullery maid in the same house.

Biddy seemed to have been terrifically excited at the prospect of the adventure to a new way of life. Much to my disappointment at the time, she no longer displayed any interest whatsoever in the Gaelic language. I told her about my new life at boarding school and it all seemed so remote to her. She was preoccupied with the thoughts of her new life in America. My midterm break was all too short as less than a week later I made the return journey to St. Andrew's accompanied by Ellie.

On my return to St. Andrew's, I settled in well and I formed a solid friendship with boisterous Bessie.

Towards the end of our Christmas break, I honoured my word and paid my first visit to Bessie and her family in Kilkenny. Papa in his wisdom, or lack of same, organised two ladies, Miss Davis and Miss Sinclair, from our local church to accompany me on my train journey there. The pair of them had to have been the most boring individuals I had ever met. I was not keen on them nor were they on me. Their only interest seemed to be that of embroidery and the condition of the crockery and table-linen at the vicarage. Neither subject interested me in the slightest. It was a joy when our journey together had ended and we had reached Kilkenny railway station where the Butler family were gathered to meet me. Miss Davis and Miss Sinclair, their duty done, more than hastily bid us Good Day and hurried off to get the return train.

My sojourn at the Butler farm was a totally novel experience for me. Up to that point in my life, I had been unaware of the existence of what was known as the 'family farm'. The Butler farm consisted of approximately one hundred acres of good arable land which was used for both dairy and tillage farming. The farmhouse itself was neither large like my home Duckworth Grove or small like the cottages on our estate.

The Butler family were extremely friendly and welcoming and at mealtime their two farm labourers sat with us at the big wooden table in their large kitchen. Bessie's mother spoke at great length about the whole concept of Gaelic culture and her love of it. I told her all about the people who lived on our estate and how some of the older ones spoke Gaelic but did not know how to write in either English or Gaelic and according to her that was quite common.

Sadly, my time with the Butlers was all too short, as Bessie and I had to return to St. Andrew's for the Hilary term. Bessie's mother and her older brother, Jack, accompanied us on our return journey there. We had so much conversation and fun on the trip and I made them laugh so much when I told them all about the boring Miss Davis and Miss Sinclair. Before long my first school year at St. Andrew's was complete and Summer stretched out ahead of me at home.

I do not remember anything of great significance that particular Summer other than joining Papa in the gardens of our home, where he lovingly examined and tended to his large collection of specimen trees, shrubs and flowers and, of course, his beloved roses that were growing both in the gardens and the woodland of our estate. Sometimes, I joined him when he went to afternoon tea at the vicarage. More often than not, I filled my days riding out with Dash, with Floss sniffing the ground as he ran along beside us.

September 1882 marked the beginning of my second year as a boarder at St. Andrew's. In addition to the subjects that we had studied during our first year, we were introduced to a new subject called Civic Awareness. This subject was an intrinsic part of our school curriculum and central to the school ethos. Of course at the time the whole concept of a school ethos was not a matter to which Bessie nor I gave much thought. Nevertheless, with or without the whole 'ethos' business, our classes with Miss Kent were fascinating. She took her role as our civic mentor very seriously. So much so, that less than two years later, during our fourth and final year at St. Andrew's, our Civic Awareness classes stretched beyond the confines of the schoolroom.

In the meantime, however, Bessie and I had already ventured into Dublin Town without permission of any sort to increase 'our civic awareness'. Both of us had feigned upset tummies and our French Teacher promptly dispatched us to the sickbay of the school. Our school matron was a doddery old dear and as soon as her back was turned we were gone. Unlike myself, Bessie had been to Dublin - according to herself - on several occasions and she was certain that she knew for sure her way about the place. I trusted her judgement and that was my folly!

We had successfully managed to get the tram to Carlyle Bridge, where we alighted from it. Bessie was certain that if we kept walking we would reach the Dublin Zoological Gardens, our intended destination. We kept walking through the streets of Dublin until eventually we arrived at the Grand Canal at Baggot Street. We kept going, passing the Royal Dublin Society and various other buildings. Bessie was absolutely positive by that stage that our destination was literally just around the corner. We turned the corner to discover - much to our astonishment - that we had arrived at Sandymount Strand, miles away from our intended destination.

We were truly lost and did not care! Both Bessie and I were almost overcome with wonder as neither of us had ever seen the coast prior to then. I can remember so clearly how the two of us stared in sheer amazement at the sight that lay before us: a beach that seemed to stretch for miles and where, intermittently, sea-gulls let out their screeching cries as they flew overhead. We hugged each other and danced around in circles, laughing and shouting. We were awestruck at the sight of the waves lapping gently along the shore and the smell of the salty air. Naturally, we were both curious to know what salt-water felt like and, without giving it a moment's thought, we ditched our shoes and stockings, hitched up our school uniforms and began paddling and splashing our feet in the sea.

I cannot recall how long we spent having such fun in that manner as we were oblivious to the passage of time. However, our enjoyment came to an abrupt end when a Dublin Metropolitan Police constable on the promenade spotted the pair of us paddling along the shoreline. Before we knew it, the two of us were seated in the back of a horse-drawn police wagon and promptly dispatched by the policeman back to St. Andrew's. Of course, it had never entered either of our heads that we would have been missed at the school, much less that the school would have reported us missing to the police. I remember it all too well. Upon our return we were immediately summonsed to the office of the Headmistress. The outcome was not to our liking as we had to spend the remainder of the week after our daily classes sitting quietly in the prayer room for three hours each evening. We were initially 'so repentant' but after a very short time we had forgotten that particular part, preferring to recall the fun we had on our adventure.

My third year at St. Andrew's was quite an unremarkable one as much of our time was devoted to prep work and I am pretty certain that our Form Tutor kept a close eye on both Bessie and myself, lest we go wandering beyond the confines of the school walls.

My final year brought with it lots of outings which were of a serious nature and contrasted sharply with my adventure to Sandymount. Our form tutor, Miss Kent, organised our class of eight into four groups of two and the purpose of the outings were to arouse our interest in philanthropic work.

I have to say that prior to then, we were all pretty much clueless to the extent of poverty in the tenements on the north side of the River Liffey. On the day of our first outing, we walked two-a-breast behind Miss Kent as she led us up the narrow alleyways and back-streets of Dublin. When we eventually reached the top of Henrietta Street, Miss Kent paused and told us to look at the sight that lay ahead of us. I saw beautiful Georgian houses which had once been home to many of Ireland's judges and barristers prior to the Act of Union 1801. Over a period of time these had become deserted by their owners who had opted instead to live in mainland Britain. The houses had fallen into decay and within a short period some of Dublin's poorest inhabitants began to crowd into these vacant buildings.

I often thought afterwards how the ragged children playing on that hard cobbled street must have felt that day when we stood looking at them from afar. We had stood observing them as though they were creatures of some sort in Dublin's Zoological Gardens. Some of them stared at us too and it was no wonder that they did so. We were an oddity from 'another world', a place where comfort and order pertained. The world of Henrietta Street which they inhabited was both filthy and foul-smelling.

Our entire class was most subdued on our return journey to St. Andrew's late that afternoon. Miss Kent felt that it was both her moral and civic duty to enlighten us to a world that differed greatly from the one that we inhabited. Due to her influence almost our entire class of eight joined the Band of Hope Ladies Charity organisation. The majority of weekends in our final year were spent organising our year-end garden fête to raise funds for the poor of inner-city Dublin.

The fête was held on the 28th of May 1885 in the grounds of our school under the guidance and direction of Miss Kent. It was a great success and we managed to raise nearly two hundred pounds for the Band of Hope. It had to have been one of the happiest days for me during my time in St. Andrew's. Everything was perfect on the day. The weather was absolutely beautiful, warm and cloud-free. We had all sorts of stalls, selling all sorts of items. I was in charge of the White Elephant Stall and I even managed to sell four chamber pots to a rather po-faced lady!

The highlight of the day for me had to have been when my former governess, Mildred, arrived at my stall. Her time in Dublin had not changed her. In fact, I think that she had become scattier than ever before. She was sporting one of her own crazy hat designs and talked as ever at a mile-a-minute in her usual bubbly manner. She told me with great enthusiasm how she had developed a love for the Gaelic language. My ears pricked up upon hearing this: Mildred was actually talking with love about the very language that had fascinated me since I was a small child and, what was even more interesting, it transpired that she was part of a little group that regularly attended Gaelic language classes in Dublin. According to her, there was a growing awareness throughout Ireland of what it meant to be Gaelic.

That night as I lay in bed I pondered over the day's happenings and my encounter with Mildred. Deep down inside me I felt that my way of thinking was at variance with what was expected of our family, the Duckworths, owners of thousands of acres of land and some of my cousins who were titled and part of Britain's gentry.

In a recent correspondence from Papa, he had told me that Georgina's mother had informed him that Georgina would be travelling to London later in the year to make her debut. I thought the whole notion was absolutely crazy and I penned a reply to Papa outlining clearly to him that I had not the remotest interest in becoming acquainted with London's High Society. That way of life did not impress me in the slightest as my four years at boarding school had opened up a whole different world to me. Although I was not yet sixteen years old, I knew that I did not desire in any form a life like

Georgina's mother and her ilk. That was a dull lifestyle.

My meeting with Mildred had unsettled me in a most pleasant way, as she, unwittingly or wittingly, had acted as a catalyst in that I was then resolutely certain that I truly wished to train to become a national school teacher. Why even as a child in my nursery, I used to line up my dolls and teach them their alphabet! Bessie could see no problem with my desire as after all her mother from time to time taught in their local National School in the County of Kilkenny. Bessie was one of those people who never saw a problem - only a solution - and she was certain that Papa would understand.

Although Bessie and I had shared the same dormitory with the same two girls for the entirety of my time in St. Andrew's, neither Bessie nor I had formed any kind of a friendship with them. They were awfully serious and both of them seemed to have had a preoccupation with etiquette, particularly Hanna, and Sybil was not much better. They were devoid of any sense of humour and more often than not the only time they spoke to Bessie or myself was to reprimand us for laughing and giggling in the dormitory at night.

On the 31st of May 1885, we graduated from St. Andrew's. It was both a sad and happy day and, according to Miss Baxter, our headmistress, we were now officially young ladies.

My time at St. Andrew's had come to an end. O'Brien, our carriage-driver, travelled from our estate with loyal and faithful Ellie and accompanied us and my luggage on the journey back home to Alm.

Chapter 3

Papa, with Floss by his side, was standing on the steps of the Grove to greet me upon my arrival. Floss as always barked and jumped with excitement upon seeing me. Customary greetings completed, I was barely in the door when Papa began speaking with enthusiasm and at great length about his success in grafting a new variety of a hybrid-tea rose. I was happy for him: after all, he had lost both my brother and Mama to death.

Papa and I then walked directly to the gardens. I have to say that I was absolutely awe-struck by Papa's creation. I was looking at almost pure perfection. Why! There in front of me was growing the deepest blood-red rose with a hue of black that I had ever laid eyes upon. It smelled of Heaven and Mama.

I could not have been home more than a day or two when I reminded Papa of my plans to become a Teacher and most certainly not a society debutante in any shape or form. Papa accepted this extremely well considering what was expected of our social class at the time. He had become very familiar with his wayward offspring. After all, my late brother William had opted for an alternative way of life in South Africa.

The following Sunday after church service, Reverend Whyte accompanied Papa and I back to the Grove to join us for Sunday luncheon. Reverend Whyte was a most entertaining individual and very little happened in Alm without his knowledge of it. My ears pricked up when he spoke about a new event which was already occurring in the village. It seems that a small group of people met weekly in the Alm church hall to attend Gaelic language classes under the tutelage of a young man by the name of Éamonn Mac Saoirse, who rode his boneshaker bicycle from Longford to Alm every week to do so. Naturally, I was extremely curious and vowed to myself there and then that I would attend the following week.

On the 11th of June 1885 I attended my first official Gaelic language class. It was rather small and it consisted of five students of which two of us were ladies.

Joy, the other lady in attendance, I thought at the time that she was pretty elderly as she was almost forty years of age. She appeared to be one of those village people that was heavily involved in both Church and village life. Her face was vaguely familiar to me as she sang in our local church choir. It transpired also that she was the teacher in the village school.

The men were a rather mixed lot. Walter from what I can remember, was an academic of some sort and it seemed that he was rather pre-occupied with the study of 'dying-languages'. He was a dull, dreary type who kept very much to himself and lived in lodgings locally. On the other hand, Patrick and Danial were both young and were very much the life and soul of the class. Patrick worked as a tailor in the village drapery whilst Danial was employed at the La Rouche Bank in Alm. They were good friends.

Patrick was a Roman Catholic and probably one of the first people of that religious persuasion that I grew to know very well as an adult. Initially Patrick, or, Pádraig as he preferred to be called, viewed me with some suspicion. He thought it pretty odd that someone like me from the Big House and Protestant should want to learn the Gaelic language. His remark annoyed me and I quickly pointed out to him that one of the principal campaigners for the restoration of the Gaelic language and the de-anglicisation of Ireland was a Church of Ireland man by the name of Douglas Hyde from our home County of Roscommon.

Pádraig told me that some members of his family had been involved in the 1867 Fenian Rising and that later his uncle was involved in the 'land war'. Like his uncle, he strongly felt that Ireland should achieve her independence from Great Britain and the ascendancy class to which I belonged should be abolished and the land given back to the small tenant farmers of Ireland. It took him a while to come to terms with the notion that I too, as an Anglo-Irish person, had just as much right to learn the Gaelic language. Pádraig's outlook unsettled me as all that 'land war' talk had done when I was a child. In spite of our diverse backgrounds, in time, we formed a solid friendship that continued up to his untimely death.

One of my truly cherished memories has to have been that of seeing Danial for the first time in our Gaelic class. He was tall, lean and handsome with a mop of black hair and green eyes. I had without doubt fallen in love with him there and then. Falling in love is one thing but if it is not reciprocated it leads to an infatuated broken heart. As I was neither too bashful nor too quiet, I reckoned that Danial had noticed my presence in our class and should he have feelings for me it would only be a matter of time before we, as Ellie would say, 'become an item'. His feelings for me had yet to be revealed.

Danial's presence in the class was an added bonus to an already most interesting subject. Mac Saoirse seemed intent in teaching us much more than the Gaelic language itself. He felt it was extremely important, too, to enlighten us regarding Gaelic culture and the history of Ireland, neither of which I was familiar with to any great extent. We were never taught Gaelic in St. Andrew's, much less Irish History. He opened my eyes to a whole new world: an Ireland steeped in folklore and tradition. He spoke too of Ancient Ireland and the warriors of old. I was fascinated by the subject matter.

Mac Saoirse felt that his little group would benefit from day trips. For our first such excursion, he had chosen Oweynagat (Cave of Cats) some miles from the village of Tulsk in the County of Roscommon. He organised our trip for the 21st of June. It was a sweltering hot day and even in our roof-topped carriage there seemed to be no shelter from the hot eye of the sun.

We arrived at Oweynagat around mid-day and were greeted by a rather small, thin old man with a crooked nose. He, it seemed, knew the history of the area extremely well as he acted as our tour guide. We followed a well-trodden Mass path which led us to the entrance of the

Cave of Cats. I was rather daunted by the prospect of entering this narrow, low and dark cave which, according to legend, led to the Underworld. Danial must have guessed my apprehension because he firmly placed his arm around my shoulder while we proceeded downward in total darkness save for the paraffin lamp that Mac Saoirse carried above his head. I felt slightly light-headed and my heart pounded so, so quickly. Was it Danial's touch or was it the peculiar surroundings? Suffice to say my heart remained racing long after we all had arrived back in Tulsk.

Mac Saoirse had organised a late luncheon for our little group at a quaint inn in the village. We sat around a hard wooden table eating our meal and recalled our ever so brief encounter with the Underworld in the Cave of Cats. On several occasions during our repast Danial and I gazed into each other's eyes. On such occasions I became oblivious to the others in our company.

That evening for almost the entire carriage journey home, Danial held my hand. It was quite an unorthodox thing to do but I did not care. In my mind's eye I could visualise the horror on Ellie's face and, should she have found out, I would have been scolded by her and, probably, chastised by Papa. Over the years, Ellie had very much taken it upon herself to act not only as a companion but as my moral guardian. She had little or no tolerance for any breach of etiquette. I seriously thought that her preoccupation with it was absolutely nonsensical. In fact, I loathed the stupidity of all it entailed and I saw little or no rationality behind such trivia. As far as Ellie was concerned I had already made a major *faux-pas* by refusing to become a society debutante in London that coming Season. I had absolutely no intention of marrying within my social class merely for the sake of ensuring my social status.

My cousin Georgina's opinion contrasted so sharply with mine: she envisaged the Season as a golden opportunity to meet a titled gentleman of means. What poppycock, I thought, as I lay in bed that night! Furthermore, as I reflect now, I am almost certain that Papa had as little regard as I for all the 'stuff and nonsense' which was expected of our social class at that time.

At breakfast the following morning, I regaled Papa with my tale of the previous day's outing and, of course, I omitted any mention of Danial in the story.

The following evening I rode Dash into the village on a small errand for Papa. As I was about to turn for home, Danial, if my memory serves me correctly, appeared it seemed out of nowhere and bade me Good Evening. I stopped directly and we spoke for some time and all the while we gazed into each other's eyes. We arranged to meet the following day in Wynn's Hotel at the top of the village for afternoon tea.

I will never forget the joy it brought to me when we met the following day. Danial and I chatted and laughed. We were without doubt in love. We continued to meet in this unconventional manner. Sometimes we met at Wynn's for tea and on other occasions we walked together along the banks of the Alm River.

Unfortunately, Ellie had made it her business to find out where I regularly disappeared to on those Summer afternoons. She confronted me when I returned home to the Grove one evening after I had been in the company of Danial. I told her all, well almost all that there was to tell. Nevertheless, Ellie was extremely curious regarding Danial's pedigree and background. She was relieved to learn from me that Danial was a first cousin of a prominent Dublin Banking family by the name of La Rouche and that his family home was on Merrion Square in Dublin. Once she had accepted that piece of information, her next query pertained to his religious persuasion. Again, she must have been relieved to know that Danial was a member of the Church of Ireland.

Despite all the years that have gone by, I still find it difficult to accept that my beloved Ellie was both a snob and a religious bigot. When I was young I did not give too much thought to Ellie's use of the word 'peasant' or 'bumpkin' when she referred to the tenant workers on our estate. The irony was that she too, for all intents and purposes, was a servant on Papa's estate.

The Summer of 1885 had to have been one of the most joyous times of my life. Mac Saoirse was a wonderful teacher and I was progressing well with my Gaelic language studies. Our class made more thoroughly enjoyable day trips with Mac Saoirse to various pre-Christian and Christian Celtic sites.

Danial and I did not restrict our meetings to Gaelic classes and day trips. Unfortunately, Ellie felt that it was her moral duty to accompany us on all other occasions. Needless to say neither Danial nor I appreciated this very much.

Occasionally Danial and I managed to rendezvous. To the best of my knowledge Papa was unaware of my dalliance with Danial and I felt it best to keep it that way for the time being. I had absolutely no idea how he would have reacted and I had no desire to upset him as he was still heart-broken over Mama's death after all the years.

It was towards the end of August that Summer when Danial told me that he was being transferred to a branch of the Bank in St. Stephen's Green in Dublin. He took the news quite stoically but, thinking back, I sometimes wonder how it really affected him. For my part, I felt that my almost perfect world had collapsed after hearing the news. I could visualise a dark lonely Winter looming ahead of me in Alm without the joy of Danial's company. Patience is a rare virtue in the mind of a fifteen year old, much less so in an impetuous young lady. I took some comfort in the fact that in a little over a year's time I too would be living in Dublin and studying at Kildare Place Teacher Training School.

In truth, I was heart-broken and extremely sad. Danial promised faithfully that he would return to Alm as often as he possibly could. He kept his word as almost every month he made the journey back to Alm and as a result became a regular guest at Wynn's Hotel.

Those brief encounters were wondrous. In fact, we even managed to sneak off on a day trip to the newly opened sea-side resort of Salthill in the County of Galway. It was my first time to see the Atlantic Ocean and what a sight it was to behold: powerful waves crashed along the infinite shore-line, white horses danced on the sea and a raw energy exuded from the air. I felt so alive and at that moment I knew without a shadow of a doubt that I belonged to this beautiful rain and windswept country.

Not only had I an insatiable appetite for this wild and sometimes barren landscape, I had an insatiable thirst for mastering not just the Gaelic language but Gaelic culture and its mythology too. In my heart I knew that Danial did not really share my passion. He actually confessed to me during our sojourn to Salthill that he had only joined Mac Saoirse's Gaelic classes in order to help relieve the boredom of living in Alm. His primary purpose for continuing classes there was that it enabled him to see me at least once a week. I was saddened to learn this and I instinctively knew that, once he had himself reestablished in the banking world of Dublin, the Gaelic world of Mac Saoirse would soon be forgotten by him.

I spent much of my time during those long, dark Winter evenings of 1885 reading whatever was available on the Gaelic language. Mac Saoirse brought along to our little group articles and papers of Gaelic interest. He told us about a Roman Catholic Canon by the name of Ulick Bourke who wrote regularly in *The Gaelic Journal*. He spoke too of Douglas Hyde who lived a relatively short distance from Alm. He mentioned that there was a possibility that we might meet these men in the future as both of them, in particular Hyde, were rapidly becoming the spokespeople for the revival of the Gaelic language. At our final class that term we sang some Gaelic songs that Mac Saoirse had taught us.

Every year, for as long as I can remember, Papa hosted the Estate Dinner on the 8th of December at the Grove for all the workers and their families. Mrs Merriman, our housekeeper, had as always organised the entire evening. Mrs Merriman was merry in name only. She had rather sharp facial features that to my mind matched to perfection her sharp, astute manner. She ran the kitchen and indeed the entire house in an efficient manner, so much so that should anyone as much as move a plate to a new location in the kitchen without her knowledge, the perpetrator of the crime was likely to receive a sharp chastisement from her. For all her idiosyncrasies, she ran the Grove like clock-work. As always, she insured that any event taking place ran seamlessly well. I loved the Estate Dinner as it was a lively affair with much dancing and merriment after the meal itself.

At our Estate Dinner that particular year, I spoke at length with Cathleen and Bart. They were still a little sad when they spoke of their eldest daughter Biddy though she had embarked on her long boat journey to America more than four years previously. They missed her and knew that they would probably never see her again. Despite their loss of Biddy to the New

World, they intended to have their Céilí on Boxing Day as ever. I was delighted when they requested my attendance at it.

My spirits were high that night as I looked forward to Danial's visit to Alm that Christmas. However, I was to be bitterly disappointed as he never did arrive. Rather he sent me a telegram which was inordinately brief: he mentioned something about the inclement weather and unsafe travel. That was it.

On Christmas Day, Reverend Whyte, joined Papa and myself for dinner at the Grove. The dreary cold weather reflected my spirits that day. During the meal Papa and Reverend Whyte spoke of the joy of Our Saviour's Birth. I shared none of their Seasonal Joy or, Goodwill, for that matter. I felt more like Scrooge from the novel *A Christmas Carol*. Within the last six months I had experienced joy and elation. However, that Christmas I was almost overcome with a forlorn sense of loss and melancholy. Although I hated admitting it to myself, my heart was broken. That night I retired early to bed and firmly resolved, broken-hearted or not, to accept the invitation from Cathleen and Bart and attend the Céilí at their home the following evening.

Up to that point in my life I was familiar with the 26th of December being called Boxing Day. However, Biddy's family referred to the day as St. Stephen's Day and a tradition of hunting the wren was common on the day. Bart and some other men from the locality dressed up for the occasion and went hunting the ditches for the wren. They were commonly known as the Wren Boys and some of them played traditional Gaelic music as they went about on their search for the little bird.

Floss and I walked the relatively short distance to the cottage. As I drew close, the smell of burning turf wafted through the still air of the night. My ears were alerted to the lively strains of fiddles and concertinas and the sounds of laughter emanating from that little home. Oh! I spent such an enjoyable evening there. After a short while I had abandoned any form of self-consciousness that I possessed and joined the little group dancing around the kitchen of that humble dwelling. As I walked home that night, with Floss in his old age limping loyally beside me, I thought of Ellie's most unkind labelling of these good people as peasants and, indeed, bumpkins. How could she, I thought, have demeaned these generous alive people in such a manner?

The following January, I resumed my studies with Mac Saoirse. There was no doubt but I still missed Danial and he never did pay a visit when the weather improved that Spring.

Pádraig by then had come to half-believe that I was genuinely interested in Gaelic culture. However, at times he was rather scathing of me particularly my accent and he didn't hesitate in reminding me. On such occasions I found his attitude tiresome and I told him so. In spite of his scepticism towards me, we communicated well on issues pertaining to Ireland. He confessed to me one evening after class that he was a member of the Irish Republican Brotherhood and he wished to see Ireland free of the shackles of the British Empire. He told me almost with a sense of joy, that he had been delighted when The Invincibles murdered Lord Frederick Cavendish the newly appointed Chief Secretary to Ireland and Thomas Burke a senior Irish Civil Servant four years previously on the 6th of May 1882, in Dublin's Phoenix Park. I was horrified by his murderous attitude and Mama's words resonated in my ears: 'Ettie always be gentle, always be kind'. Yet, I had begun to understand that Ireland should be an independent country, free of English rule.

I was just sixteen years old and I was in a state of confusion: I was not English like some of my cousins on the Mainland, I was not Irish like Biddy's family. So, where did I fit? Papa and people like us were often referred to as the Anglo-Irish Ascendancy by the London media at the time. But that was not true and neither was it false. My life contrasted sharply with that of my cousin Georgina. It seemed to me that she fitted neatly into her role as a debutante in the aristocratic circle of the United Kingdom, whilst, I had already become almost fluent in a language that was viewed in some quarters as the tongue of the patriotic Irish. In addition, I had shunned to a large extent the notion of passing my days socially interacting with only my own social class.

This wet and windswept island was my home, the only country I knew, and little did I realise at the time that it was on the cusp of a wave of nationalism that would sweep over it in the following few decades.

Chapter 4

Around that time, I had a rather long and copious letter from Bessie and of course I was delighted as ever to have heard from her. Needless to say, Bessie as you know never viewed an issue as a problem and as far as she was concerned there had to have been an answer to everything. Without doubt she had a most optimistic view of the world. Simply nothing deterred her. So much so that she had applied for a position in the Civil Service administration in Dublin. It was a bold step as it employed very few women at the time. Bessie had very strong opinions in relation to the subordinate position of women in Irish society. She found it almost insufferable to think that she as a woman had not the same voting rights as a man.

In her letter Bessie described at great length how she had made contact with Anna Haslam who was the leader of the newly formed Dublin Women's Suffrage Association and that she fully intended becoming a member of the

Association. She was much nearer the voting age of twenty-one, than I, although we were in the same Form at St. Andrew's. In addition, her letter truly confirmed in my mind what I had always thought and felt about her: that she was the type of person who was destined for great things as she was such a fearless and pioneering individual. I was not too surprised by the contents of her letter, after all Bessie came from a pretty unconventional family in the County of Kilkenny.

Ellie was firmly ensconced in our household. However, there were times when she and Mrs Merriman found themselves at loggerheads over the most trivial of issues. Mrs Merriman was quite entrenched in her ways and viewed her role as house-keeper as pivotal to the smooth functioning of day-to-day events at the Grove. She quite openly belittled Ellie and in her mind could see no justification in Ellie's continued employment with us.

Poor Ellie, who had without question devoted her entire life to our family! She first came to work for us as scullery maid when she was fifteen years old. After my brother William's birth some eleven years later, Mama employed a nanny for him. Apparently she proved to be totally unsatisfactory and Mama sacked her. Ellie had loved my brother from the day he was born and her devotion to him had not gone unnoticed by Mama at the time. So much that Ellie found herself in the elevated position of becoming the new nanny to William. From what I can recall William loved her dearly too. Indeed, years later he often referred to her in a most warm and affectionate manner in his correspondence from The Transvaal.

Now that I had grown-up I still needed Ellie as much as ever. She was my companion and despite her sometimes narrow-minded and bigoted ways I loved her just as dearly. After Danial had 'let me down' so to speak it was she who listened to my tales of woe. So as far as I was concerned Mrs Merriman could just simply mind her own business and leave poor old Ellie alone and I told her so.

In the Summer of 1886, Bessie came to stay at the Grove for the first time. I was truly delighted at the prospect of her arrival. She literally arrived out of the blue one August afternoon. She had given neither Papa nor I any prior notice. She had made the entire rail and carriage journey from Kilkenny via Dublin to Alm unaccompanied. Upon her arrival in Alm she then walked almost three miles to the Grove. Poor Ellie was astounded at the very thought of a young lady doing such a wayward thing. Papa was simply shocked and I in truth was not totally surprised at Bessie's outlandish behaviour. It was so, so wonderful to see her. She stayed with us at the Grove for almost a fortnight and during that time we had such great times.

Bessie was an extremely independent person and had very much grown up with the idea that women were very much equal to men and, therefore, should have the same rights and freedom as any man. I must say that I had always noticed her very independent personality when we were at St. Andrew's and, maybe, that is why we became such good friends. In many ways my childhood at the Grove had been a very sheltered one and as a result I knew little of the ways of the world. Even when Bessie and I were boarders in St. Andrew's, she was forever pushing out the bounds of the school rules.

Bessie found our way of life at the Grove to be a little strange. She never knew up to then that we had so many servants and she thought it was rather amusing and indeed odd. Odd as she found it, I am sure that Papa must have been totally bemused to find Bessie in the milking parlour engaged in an in-depth conversation about our Jersey cows with our herdsman regarding the merits of the breed. Bessie knew that she had not a remote possibility of inheriting the family farm in Kilkenny and that it would most likely go to her eldest brother, Jeff. She was a very diverse individual. Let me explain: one moment she had the ability to behave like a rather helpless young lady and a moment later she could argue her case as good as any man. She was quite determined to obtain a position in the Government administration in Dublin Castle and she did just that.

I must say that I was truly delighted that Bessie spent almost the entire month of August at the Grove with Papa and me. Come September of that same year, Bessie accompanied me to Dublin where I was about to commence my Teacher Training at Kildare Place.

Before we embarked on our journey from the Grove to Dublin Bessie upset me as she told me that as far as she was concerned Floss's days were numbered. Indeed, Floss was an old dog but I had never really noticed how bedraggled he had become and even though he was almost blind and limping I loved him dearly and dreaded the thought of the Grove without him. I was slightly apprehensive as well at the thought of journeying to Dublin without dear Ellie at my side. As self-assured as Bessie was, she was certainly no substitute for soft-spoken Ellie. Bessie had absolutely no idea how anxious I was, much less she may not have understood. I remember thinking at the time how easy it would have been to abandon the whole notion of embarking on the Teacher training course. After all, it was virtually unheard of for a member of my social class to work. My cousin Georgina was following the exact path that was expected of her, contrasting so sharply with me.

I was initially quite unsettled at Kildare Place. Unlike St. Andrew's there was no dorm sharing. Rather each of us had a room to ourselves. As a result of this there was far less social interaction between us and it was lonely. We had the privilege once a week to attend theatre or some other social event. Privilege or not, it was pretty awful for the first month or so, as I had not as yet formed a friendship of any kind with my fellow scholars. Looking back, I think that we were all pretty much in the same boat. Our mentor, Miss Cauldwell, must have noticed as she organised an afternoon for myself and the five other freshmen to attend the Gaiety Theatre to see a matinée performance of the comic play written by the playwright Oliver Goldsmith *She Stoops to Conquer*. It was thoroughly enjoyable and we all laughed so much. We then went to the nearby Shelbourne Hotel for evening tea. I think that our outing must have acted as an icebreaker as consequently we all became much more relaxed and friendly towards each other.

Shortly after, I became quite friendly with both Margaret Belmont and Mary Rollo. Our newly formed friendships continued for the duration of our two-year course and, indeed, long after we had left Kildare Place.

Mary, Margaret and I really maximised our free time from study. It was terrific and I certainly enjoyed my new-found freedom. Mary knew Dublin Town extremely well as her family home was located on North Great George's Street. She regularly brought both Mary and myself to her home for tea on Tuesday afternoons.

Without doubt, we almost always had a terrific time there. Her mother was really funny and ever so lazy. More often than not when Mary brought both Margaret and myself to her home, her mother inevitably seemed to be entertaining her friends. This mainly took the form of card-playing and it would end abruptly before Mary's father would return from Dublin Castle where he worked as a senior Government official. Apparently, he totally disapproved of card-playing of any sort.

Mary had one sibling, an older sister called Catherine, who sadly was confined to sitting in her chair as she was severely crippled and could neither stand, much less walk. It seemed that she spent her days indoors painting with watercolours. However, she really enjoyed a jaunt about Dublin Town in her pushchair and frequently on a sunny Tuesday afternoon we drove Catherine in her pushchair about the town. She particularly liked to visit St. Stephen's Green to see the ducks in the pond.

It was on one of those occasions that I almost literally bumped into Danial. Our little party was nearing the top of Grafton Street and close to the junction opposite the main gates of the entrance to St. Stephen's Green when, as if he had appeared out of nowhere, Danial stood before me. My heart raced as it had done that day back when he first put his arm on my shoulder during the trip with Mac Saoirse to the Oweynagat. I was dumbstruck and stood there, staring at him with highly charged and mixed emotions. In what seemed like a second, waves of sadness coupled with delight and even anger raced through my system all at once. How could he have failed to honour his word and fail to visit me that Christmas at my home in Alm? All such thoughts swirled around in my head. My companions must have sensed my unease as they engaged him in conversation whilst I stood there silent, too overcome with emotion to speak. I wanted to run. Yet, I wanted to stay. I was almost in a state of panic. Worse again, he seemed to be engaged in conversation with the others in a relaxed fashion. It was so humiliating. I felt as though he had never known me. I felt so dreadful and helpless.

Catherine saved the day so to speak as she became unsettled in her pushchair and cried out for us to bring her to the duck pond. With that he hastily bade our little group Good Day and hurried off out of sight into a rather crowded Grafton Street. For the remainder of our outing that day I withdrew into myself, wishing that the day was over and that my encounter with Danial had never occurred. I was very unsettled for quite some time afterwards and more often than not I declined my companions' invitation to join them on our free Tuesday afternoons, opting instead to remain in the college reading. I continued in that manner for almost the remainder of the term.

On the 15th of December that year I made the journey home unaccompanied for the first time. I was so delighted to see Papa standing on the steps of the Grove to greet me. However, there was no sign of my beloved Floss. Papa must have guessed my concern as almost immediately he directed me into the drawing room where Floss was lying in his basket and Ellie was gently coaxing him to drink some milk. Tears flowed down my face as I looked at my feeble old friend who had barely the strength to wag his tail. However, when I bent down he looked at me through his half blind eyes and managed to lick my hand. I spent almost the entirety of the following three days on an armchair beside his basket. I was distraught at the thoughts of life without my little four legged friend. On the 18th of December I held him for the last time as his head drooped on my arm and passed on to the Dogs' Heaven in the sky. That same place that had stolen both Mama and William.

I returned to Kildare Place after Christmas for the next semester. I had resolved to myself that I would fully embrace life again. I did just that. Bessie had recently taken up employment working in an administrative capacity in Dublin Castle and during my free time from Kildare Place I often met up with her. She was already familiar with a group who met regularly in a small hotel on Molesworth Street to speak Gaelic and discuss the history and culture of Ireland. Needless to say, I was overjoyed at the prospect of becoming a member too and for the remainder of my first year at Kildare Place I spent my free Sunday afternoons in the company of Bessie and the fine people of the

Gaelic group. On the other hand I spent the majority of my free Tuesday afternoons in the company of Mary and Margaret when it became almost habitual for us to take Catherine in her pushchair on outings around Dublin Town. We even brought her to the Dublin Zoological Gardens, the very place that Bessie and I had attempted in vain to journey to during our time in Saint Andrew's. I remember so well being extremely disappointed and indeed, saddened to have seen magnificent large animals confined to rather small enclosures. I remember too how they all seemed so bored, as we humans stared at them. However, Catherine was absolutely ecstatic as every so often she clapped her hands and let out screams of delight. It was hard to tell what she thought most of the time as speech was almost impossible for her. However, on that occasion the three of us were pretty certain that Catherine was indeed very happy.

I did not allow myself the time, much less the luxury, to dwell on thoughts of Danial. Realistically, I could have bumped into him frequently during my time in Kildare Place as his place of employment, La Rouche Bank, St. Stephen's Green was located a relatively short distance from our Training College. I had successfully managed to think of him less and less. However, I did indeed get an unpleasant surprise when I read the announcement of his engagement in *The Times* newspaper in the month of May that year. Any glimmer of hope regarding a renewed familiarity between Danial and I now was impossible.

Arriving home to the Grove that Summer was so different from ever before as Papa now stood alone on the steps to greet me. Gone was the familiar sight of Floss at his side. Maybe, I was imagining it but I noticed for the first time that Papa had aged. Aged or not, he spoke with the same enthusiasm as ever regarding his gardens and various up-coming flower shows.

After dinner that evening we sat in the library and discussed at length the very topical issue of landlord / tenant relations. What struck me at the time was his stoic manner regarding the possible demise of the ascendancy class. He had a terrific insight into the current situation in this country. He was certain that there was a mounting degree of nationalism in many forms occurring on the Island at the time. Indeed, he expressed little or no surprise when I told him that I knew a chap who was a member of the Irish Republican Brotherhood.

That evening, I felt for the first time that Papa viewed me as an adult. I was truly delighted when later he paid me a wonderful compliment as he told me I had become so like my dear Mama as apparently she was quite a spirited individual in her youth. Sadly, I was never privy to really knowing her as she had been ill for the all too short length of time I had known her.

Mac Saoirse's Gaelic classes had ended temporarily for the Summer months. Apparently, he was spending that time cycling around Connemara becoming even more familiar with Gaelic customs and ways. Nevertheless, the members of his Gaelic class in Alm continued to meet in Wynn's Hotel and converse together in Gaelic. It was great to be back home and I re-joined them as soon as I possibly could. Pádraig was a very charismatic individual and in a very short period of time he became the informal leader of the group in the absence of Mac Saoirse. He was ambitious too as he had planned to move to Dublin that Autumn where he had been offered a senior position in a well-known department store on Sackville Street. According to himself that move to Dublin would give him a greater opportunity to advance Ireland's independence from the United Kingdom.

In early September of that year, both Pádraig and I travelled by train together to Dublin as he was going to commence work there with his new employer. I was returning to the Teacher College for my second and final year. Of course, Ellie, true to form was anything but pleased to see the company I was keeping and she found no difficulty in telling me so. On the other hand, Papa reserved his judgement as he probably knew all too well that I was too headstrong, or, maybe it was simply that he loathed as much as

I did the mindless conventions that existed within our social class.

My final year in Teacher Training differed considerably from first year there as almost my entire academic year consisted of monitored teaching under the guidance of an Educational Inspector in a national school located on Marlborough Street in Dublin Town. The school was both mixed in terms of gender and indeed social class. However, the vast majority of the school pupils lived locally and many of them came from impoverished homes. These young boys and girls reminded me vividly of the children I had seen some years previously playing on the street outside the tenements of Henrietta Street.

Unlike our first year, there were few sanctions and our free time from the classroom was very much our own. Mary, Margaret and I went on lots of outings to various places and various events.

The Phoenix Park became a pretty regular haunt for us and on such occasions we would bring

Catherine along in her push-chair with us. She especially loved to watch and listen to the musicians who played regularly at the Band Stand. It made her so happy and she frequently hit the arms of the push-chair in glee. It was wonderful to see her so joyful, as life could not have been easy for her. Mary loved her older sister dearly and often remarked that Catherine was one of God's special children.

Needless to say upon my return to Dublin that Autumn I re-joined the Sunday Gaelic group in Molesworth Street. I could not help but note to myself the odd position Bessie was in: she was employed by the English administration in Dublin at that time, yet she had within less than a year become one of the leading figures in Dublin for the restoration of the Gaelic language in Irish life.

Pádraig and I kept in regular contact and within a short space of time he too, attended the Sunday Gaelic group. Both Bessie and he became quite friendly with each other. Indeed they had become romantically involved and shared the notion of Ireland's independence from the United Kingdom with strong leanings towards the Irish Republican Brotherhood. As well as I knew Bessie, I was never privy to her level of involvement in that organisation. Even though Bessie and I had been friends since St. Andrew's there were aspects of her life that I absolutely knew little or nothing about. Maybe it was just as well that I was ignorant of such.

The gods must have been favourably disposed towards me as I was thoroughly enjoying life and in May of 1888 I qualified as a national school teacher. Of course, there were times when I thought of Danial and I was relieved that I had not encountered him again. Yet, there was still a little voice in my head saying otherwise.

Chapter 5

Papa travelled to Dublin on the 26th of May 1888 to attend my graduation ceremony at Kildare Place and stayed at the Shelbourne Hotel which was quite close by. I was absolutely delighted to see him as he rarely left Alm since Mama's demise. We dined together the evening of my graduation and he spoke rather a lot about his school pal, Parnell, who, it appeared, had become embroiled in a political scandal. Apparently, according to an article in *The Times* newspaper, Parnell had condoned the Phoenix Park Murders of 1882. Papa thought such news was rather unsettling and indeed strange as he was pretty certain that Parnell was quite constitutional in his behaviour.

Papa also expressed grave concern regarding the future of our home, Duckworth Grove. It seemed to him that the relationship between landlord and tenant was changing. This was being brought about through various Land Acts at Parliament in Westminster. These Acts prescribed changes in land ownership and the

Land Commission, established some years previously by the Government, was tasked with implementation. I fully understood Papa's concern as many large estates like our home Duckworth Grove were now being bought by the Land Commission and the lands redistributed among the small tenant farmers. Such changes did not bode well for the future of Duckworth Grove as my home.

Needless to say the evening with Papa would not have been complete without Papa speaking about his roses and the prospect of winning an award from one or more of them. He was never daunted, and he firmly believed that his 'Rose of Alm' would win the Gold Medal yet.

In 1891, Papa's dream was realised as he was awarded the much coveted Gold Medal by the Royal Horticultural Association of the British Isles for his 'Rose of Alm'. Papa was overjoyed and, for almost the first time since Mama's death all those years ago, he was genuinely optimistic about life in general. So much so that he contemplated the notion of purchasing a townhouse in Dublin. Of course, I was absolutely delighted with such news.

That year too, Papa's school pal, Parnell died, he who had contributed so much to Ireland's cause for social justice and the man who was often referred to in the newspapers as 'Ireland's Uncrowned King'. The day of his funeral was declared a national day of mourning. Thousands lined the streets of Dublin to pay their final respects. Bessie and I stood in silence with hoards of other people on College Green and bowed our heads as the funeral cortege passed.

Around that time I lived as a boarder in Mrs Miller's house and had come to reside with her after qualifying as a national school teacher. Mrs Miller's residence was located on Leinster Road, in Rathmines. I purchased a ladies boneshaker bicycle and used it daily to pedal to my place of employment on Marlborough Street which coincidentally was the same school where I had done my final year's training.

I resided with Mrs Miller for almost ten years. My accommodation contrasted sharply with my accommodation in Kildare Place as I had the entire second floor of her home. It was spacious and spacious and all as it was, it was small when compared to the Grove. Mrs Miller was a middle-aged widow and had only one other occupant in her home and that was her large marmalade cat called Duke. It was the most unfriendly creature known to mankind. Yet, she spoke to it as if it were human. As far as I was concerned it was contemptuous of the human race and even Mrs Miller herself. Duke's attitude did not bother her in the slightest as she was such a jolly individual and possessed a terrific sense of humour.

She seemed to know everybody's business as often times, when I would arrive back to Mrs Miller's, after a particularly gruelling day in school, she would regale me with lots of gossip and tales of the day's events in the neighbourhood. She loved company and frequently invited my friends to supper.

The whole concept of Gaelic culture was alien to her and she often remarked to me that I was simply quite crazy pursuing such interests. I had a clear recollection - at the time that Douglas Hyde established Conradh na Gaeilge in 1894 - that she thought I was simply potty to be involved with such an odd organisation. After all she remarked that 'The King doesn't speak Gaelic. Therefore, it must be a useless language'. It was too tiresome to have attempted to explain my ideals and interests to her and I never did.

I was enjoying life as I had my daily routine well established and I found my work as a national school teacher rewarding. In fact, I had become such a creature of habit that I had little space in my head to contemplate loneliness or sadness, much less shock or surprise.

This was to change radically as on the 24th of March that year I accidently met Danial for the first time after so many years. Though it had been rather a non-eventful day at school, I was deep in thought about an upcoming school event. In any case, I was pedaling my boneshaker along Nasseau Street when I nearly rode over him as he was attempting to cross from one side of the street to the other.

Both of us stopped and stared at each other. I was lost for words. All emotional attachment I had to him came flooding back. I even remember tears welling up in my eyes. Eventually, I did manage to mutter something that vaguely resembled a salute. I think he was as dumbfounded as I. After what at the time seemed to be an eternity of mumbles and mutterings we eventually agreed to go for afternoon tea to the Shelbourne Hotel there and then.

Though we were a bit uncomfortable at the start of our tea, after a time we were 'back' to those afternoons which we had spent in Wynn's Hotel in Alm and we were laughing and talking with the same enthusiasm as we shared back then in the sun-filled days of our youth.

Later that evening we parted company: he to join his wife and baby son at their home on

course, Pádraig had always professed such leanings. Bessie divided much of her spare time between Conradh na Gaeilge and the Dublin Women's Suffrage Society. Needless to say, she was overjoyed in the Spring of 1899 when 85 women were elected as Poor Law Guardians following the extension of franchise to women at local government level. That according to Bessie acted as a first step on the road for full franchise to women.

1899 proved to be a very eventful year for me. With very little persuasion from Bessie, I joined Maud Gonne's newly formed women's organisation Inghinidhe na hÉireann (Daughters of Ireland). I truly loved being part of a movement which both taught and fostered the Gaelic language and much more besides. We learned Irish Dancing and indeed, joined its drama group, too. We were so lucky, as W. B. Yeats even wrote a play for us to perform and we even had a visit from Mac Saoirse, my Gaelic teacher, in Alm to see our stage performance. Needless to say, I was so committed to

Inghinidhe na hÉireann that once again I had little time to dwell on thoughts of Danial.

I was pleasantly surprised that year when I encountered Mildred again. She too joined Inghinidhe na hÉireann and she was extremely committed to its dramatic branch and, in addition, to that she spent much time campaigning for the establishment of a national theatre in Dublin Town. She was as outlandish in her manner of dress as ever. She even managed to stitch her political opinions to bits of paper which were perched around her daft hat. Oh! She was such a funny individual. I do not think she ever intentionally set out to cause a stir but inevitably she did. A prominent Dublin water-colour painter by the name of J. B. Rock was totally captivated by her and, after much persuasion on his part, Mildred became his lover. Her level of devotion to him was questionable.

Mildred was highly fickle by nature and her commitment to either people or causes usually had a passionate but rather brief life-span.

Looking back, it was a wonder that she remained in Duckworth Grove as my governess, for the duration of time that she did.

In July of the same year, Papa acquired a motor car. It was a remarkable object as it could literally be driven on any roadway at any time. Oh! My gosh! It went so, so fast. Papa could make that machine motor at 20mph and what was more, he drove it himself. He was so daring! Since Papa had acquired that motor car, he visited me frequently in Dublin and I absolutely loved those occasions.

Papa never needed a reason to take his motor car for a jaunt and, on one such occasion, we travelled to visit Aunt Edith and Uncle Arthur at their home Tudorham House, in the County of Down. I must confess I found the entire sojourn there extremely tiresome.

By that stage in my life, my way of thinking had departed greatly from theirs. Neither Uncle Arthur, much less Aunt Edith, could comprehend or understand Gaelic language or culture. As far as they were concerned the language and ways of the United Kingdom of Great Britain and Ireland were supreme and any notion of deviance from that mode of thinking needed to be crushed. They were staunch Unionists. Nor did they make sense of the fact that I had taken a position in Dublin as a teacher. Worse again, I had blatantly refused some years previously to become a society debutante in London. Aunt Edith seemed to have had some bizarre notion that I had 'missed out', unlike their daughter, my cousin Georgina who had married an extremely wealthy North of England industrialist.

I almost felt sorry for the trivial mentality of Aunt Edith as she had to overcome the fact that her daughter had married a man who lacked a title and a pedigree and, unfortunately, his was 'new money'. Her attitude did not surprise me, as I remembered the time during my childhood when Harold and Georgina had stayed with Papa and me at the Grove. As young as she was, she possessed all the trappings of snobbery which no doubt she had 'inherited' from her mother, Aunt Edith.

We stayed with Aunt Edith and Uncle Arthur for almost a week. During our time there with them we made two very enjoyable trips, one to the Glens of Antrim and the other to the Giants Causeway. Both were spectacular.

The Glens of Antrim reminded me of the fairy tale *Hansel and Gretel*. Papa and I walked in that densely wooded forest, surrounded by enormous Sitka spruce, native oak and beech trees that grew there. Papa was truly in his element, whilst Arthur and Edith sat in the nearby Glenmount Hotel and, no doubt, Arthur was sampling the cognac on offer there.

Again when we journeyed to the Giants Causeway, the pair of them declined our invitation to walk along that geographical wonder. They opted instead to dine in a tavern nearby.

In truth, I had little in common with them and that clearly became more apparent as the week wore on. On the final evening of our sojourn at their home, what should have been a jolly occasion, instead erupted into near disaster! As the week there had progressed, I had found it increasingly difficult to listen to her disparaging remarks about Irish people coupled with her prejudices against them. So much so, that by the time it came to the eve of our departure, I contained myself no longer. Up to that point I had struggled to refrain from 'letting fly' and telling her what I thought of her utterly bigoted ways and that was mainly because Papa had warned me to 'be quiet'. As far as I was concerned, enough was enough! I must have shocked the spectacles off her 'stuck up nose' when I informed her of my Love of almost all aspects of Irish culture and language and that furthermore, I was a fluent Gaelic speaker and I had friends in the Irish Republican Brotherhood. Of course, I did not upset her further by telling her that her dear husband, my uncle, had a mistress in Dublin. Let her live in her arrogant ignorance.

I think Papa was highly embarrassed by my Republican outburst. Frankly I did not care what anybody thought, as I knew for certain that night that I had nailed my colours to the mast and they certainly were not red, white and blue.

Chapter 6

In December of 1899, Papa had purchased a detached, red-brick townhouse on Conyngham Road in Dublin. I absolutely loved it. It was by no means as large, or as rambling, as the Grove but, it was still quite spacious. Papa maintained that he only required two servants to manage it and he employed a married couple by the name of Mary and John Collins, who hailed from near the little village of Palmerstown which was located four miles west of our new residence. Oh! They were such lovely people and they had one ten year old sweet-natured child by the name of Jack. Their quarters were within the house itself, unlike Duckworth Grove.

By that stage, I had become very used to looking after myself mainly due to my time spent with Mrs Miller. I no longer viewed servants as 'servants', rather I viewed them more like family members of sorts.

We had a most beautiful view of the River Liffey from the back of the house and with more than a little prompting from me, Papa named it *Radharc na Life*.

A little less than twenty years previously, Mildred had frightened me somewhat when she announced to me that the era of the Big House was coming to an end. Her predictions proved true as government in Westminster had enacted various Land Acts. In addition, the Land Commission had been established by the Government in 1881 in order to purchase vast tracts of land such as that of Duckworth Grove. I think that policy came as a relief to Papa as he availed of the opportunity and sold almost three quarters of the estate to the Land Commission in 1897. Thus, some of the monies released from the sale of the land enabled him to purchase both a motor car and *Radharc na Life* by 1899.

Heretofore, I had always celebrated Christmas at the Grove. However, Papa and I elected to spend Christmas 1899 in our newly acquired Dublin home. Oh! It was so different. It totally lacked the formality that was part and parcel of life at the Grove. In fact, Papa even organised a New Year's Party at our new residence and it was so informal. I thoroughly enjoyed that night as many of my friends were invited, too.

Pádraig even brought along his friend Christy and I am certain that Papa was slightly taken aback at my motley collection of friends. I must confess that I was extremely curious about Christy. He hailed from the area of Gardiner Street and had the strongest Dublin accent which nearly 'cut the ear' off a more than a little surprised Papa. In addition, he seemed to lack finesse when it came to the rudiments of dining etiquette. I remember so well the confused look on his face as he tried to figure out which spoon or knife to use at the meal. He could have shoved ten forks into his mouth at once that night. It did not matter! I was captivated by his wit and his passion for this little rain and windswept island. Into the bargain, he was tall and athletic with fair, scraggly hair and a beard. At the time, I did not want to admit to myself, much less to him, that I had fallen in love with him of sorts. In time, despite our contrasting backgrounds we became 'an item'.

Christy was the eldest of a family of eight children. His father worked as a maintenance man in the newly formed Dublin Tramway Company and his mother was employed from time to time as a charlady. They lived in a two-roomed tenement off Gardiner Street. Despite the fact that they were poor, both of his parents had an air of dignity about them.

Christy's father held very strong opinions regarding the need for his children to receive an education. He viewed formal education as the means for his family to improve their life's lot. Unlike many of the women and men in their neighbourhood, both Christy's father and, to a lesser extent, his mother were literate. All that aside, I did get some shock when I visited their home for the first time. It happened quite unexpectedly really.

It had been a particularly tiring day at school and I remained there long after classes had ended and my pupils had returned home. It was almost six o'clock when I finally had fully organised the upcoming trip to the Dublin Zoological Gardens for the class. I left the school building and began pedaling my way towards *Radharc na Life* and, as I did, I met Christy on Sackville Street. He was returning home after his day's work where he was employed as a compositor with the *Irish Informer* newspaper. Why! There and then, he invited me to his parents' home for supper that evening. Initially, I declined. However, after some persuasion on his part, I agreed.

We made our way up Sackville Street towards the area where Christy and his family lived. The whole place reminded me so much of the time Miss Kent had brought our school Form to see the dreadful living conditions of Dublin's poor. I concealed my disdain to the best of my ability to Christy, after all this godforsaken place was home to him.

Their home was located in the basement of a Georgian tenement house. I remember vividly how Christy's younger brothers and sisters stared at me. It felt to me, at the time, that it was like a mixture of contempt and curiosity on their part. His mother was a small thin woman with a hard, world weary expression on her face. She offered me a cup of tea with a roughly cut piece of bread. I ate it as best I could. Neither she, nor I, were comfortable in each other's company and barely a word passed between us.

Christy must have sensed my unease as he drew my attention to a makeshift box which contained a collie type dog and her three pups which was situated in the corner of their dull brown, ill-lit living room. The mother of the pups sat there wagging her tail. Both she and her pups were truly beautiful. Needless to say, I fell in love with them all. I was enthralled by the smallest and probably the weakest one of the litter. The little darling had a black patch over her left eye. I picked up the little dote. Christy smiled and nodded. Why! There and then, little Mollie had a new owner and that was me.

From what I can remember, I am almost certain that I left shortly after that with Mollie in my arms and Christy walked my bicycle beside me.

We walked along together, almost in silence. I was lost in thought. I could not help thinking of Ellie's reaction the time when she had found out about my relationship with Danial those years ago back home in Alm. Danial, in her mind, was a suitable individual for me to 'walk out with'. Afterall, he was a member of a prestigious banking family and, furthermore, he was of 'good Protestant stock'. Christy on the other hand, was poor and a Catholic, with pretty radical notions regarding Ireland's future freedom from the might of the British Empire. I had visions too of Papa and how he might well perceive Christy.

Christy must have guessed my mood as he accompanied me back to *Radharc na Life* because later that evening, before he returned to his home, he told me that he would not have been surprised had I wished to 'have no more to do with him'. After all, according to him we 'were from worlds apart'. I remember well how I disregarded his silly comment as I viewed him as an individual with both principles and ideals. Not only that, but he made me laugh and I loved to do just that.

Needless to say, thoughts of Danial niggled away somewhere at the back of my mind and as ever I pushed those thoughts out of my head. Nevertheless, a niggling curiosity mingled with a wave of sadness remained that refused to exit my head.

Worlds apart or not, Christy became a regular visitor to *Radharc na Life* and often stayed for tea. Mary, our housekeeper, frequently remarked to me that Christy was a 'good lad' and 'a fine cut of a young man'. Her comment pleased me. To some it would have seemed that she was speaking out of turn. However, in truth, it reflected Mary's almost motherly interest in my wellbeing.

Papa still had a permanent retinue of servants at Duckworth Grove. They lived nearby in the servants' quarters on the estate. In contrast,

Mary and, her husband, John, were our only live-in employees at *Radharc na Life.* The additional workers that were required lived out and attended for work on a daily basis.

We had a regular charlady by the name of Annie who lived close by on Manor Street. She was a really thin little woman who went around with a cigarette permanently dangling from her mouth and cursed like an army Fusilier. She was such a loud character. I often overheard her in the kitchen telling Mary the most hair-raising stories about soldiers from the nearby barracks and their dalliances with the local prostitutes. It was on occasions like that I remembered how tranquil life had been with Mrs Miller and her nasty cat, Duke, who far out-lived the nine lives allocated to him.

We had turned the corner into the twentieth century. Rapid change was taking place not alone in Ireland but throughout Europe and the British Empire. Nationalism was firmly ensconced in the psyche of many Irish men and women and I was in the throes of it. My active membership of Conradh na Gaeilge insured that I was frequently in contact with characters who were committed to Ireland's Cause for Freedom in its many guises.

Why, Mildred was absolutely ecstatic when finally we had a national theatre, known as the *Abbey Theatre,* which opened its doors for the first time in 1904. I remember that night so, so well. Yeats even premiered his new play *On Baile's Strand* that night there. Needless to say the opening of the theatre was a momentous occasion in Dublin and as a result it drew a highly varied audience. I was shocked and more than a little surprised when, during the interval, I met with Danial and his pregnant wife in the foyer of the theatre. After he had introduced her to me, she stood there close beside him and did not utter a word. Then she hastily excused herself and returned into the theatre's auditorium.

Danial and I stood alone, together uncomfortable, yet gazing into each other's eyes as we spoke. Time had done nothing for me as the familiar pangs of desire were there as fresh and as alive as they were when we had first met more than ten years previously in Mac Saoirse's Gaelic class. It almost came as a relief when the interval was over. I bade him Good Night and returned, alone, with a heavy heart to my seat beside Bessie and the rest of the Conradh group.

Not too long after my night at the Abbey, I had a letter from my cousin Georgiana to say that she and her husband were coming to Dublin, as he had some business to attend to there. I was delighted at the prospect of seeing her again. We had seen very little of each other since her marriage as she lived in Sheffield in the North of England. I met up with her in the Gresham Hotel on Sackville Street for afternoon tea where they were residing for the duration of their sojourn in Dublin.

It did not take long to establish that she and I had become totally estranged from each other: our lives were so, so dissimilar. She appeared to be very content in the role as a wife and mother. She was extremely puzzled to learn from me that I had neither a desire for marriage and much less to have children. I attempted, almost in vain, to explain to her that I loved my work as a teacher and I was quite content living in *Radharc na Life* with my little dog, Mollie and staff. She genuinely failed to understand my situation coupled with the fact that according to her 'I had peculiar notions about Ireland's Cause'. She quizzed me thoroughly about Christy and she was a little horrified to learn of his pedigree, or should I say lack of pedigree! She seemed to be genuinely concerned, too, regarding the future of Duckworth Grove and was slightly aghast and fearful for its future. She felt it was her duty to inform me that Duckworth Grove needed an heir. Frankly I did not care too much about its future. I did not wish to hurt her feelings and inform her that the days of the power of the Ascendancy class were numbered.

Why! Only the previous year at Westminster Parliament, the Chief Secretary, George Wyndham, had successfully passed into law a

Land Act that virtually saw the demise of the large estates in many counties as vast tracts of land were purchased by the Government and parcelled out to former tenant farmers. It was less than a year since that Land Act had been passed into law and its effects were already visible. In my home County of Roscommon, Lord Totingborough of Castle Dullor and family had sold their Castle and entire estate to the Land Commission for a sizeable sum of money and had moved to England.

Chapter 7

Christy was very much a person of habit. Every Tuesday night he attended Arthur Griffith's newly formed movement *Sinn Féin* with his friend Pádraig. He visited *Radharc na Life* on Thursday nights, coming directly from his place of employment when he finished work at six o' clock in the evening. So it was some disappointment to me when he failed to visit one particular Thursday at his usual time. It emerged that instead he had gone to Liberty Hall with his father to listen to the prominent Trade Union Leader, James Larkin.

Larkin, prior to then, had been very active organising the workers in Liverpool and Belfast. He had then come to Dublin with the intention of forming an Irish Transport and General Workers Union. He successfully formed the Union and also became its general secretary.

Christy's employer frowned greatly upon the concept of trade union membership as did his father's employer. As a result both of them were in very precarious positions at their respective places of work. The situation angered both men as their employers were in inordinate positions of strength. Christy's father was particularly vulnerable as, aside for Christy, he was the only bread-winner in the family. Neither of Christy's brothers were employed and his sisters were far too young to go out to work. He had one of the lowliest positions in the tram company as a coach cleaner and, he knew that he could be replaced at a moment's notice.

The unemployment rate was very high in Dublin and, for many of those in work, their working conditions were pretty awful. They were expected to work outrageously long hours for a meagre wage coupled with the fact that their employment could be terminated at any time without notice of any form. Ironic as it may seem, it reminded me so much of the time of the Land War that occurred in the County of Mayo during my childhood at the Grove.

As always the school year ended at the beginning of the month of July and I resolved to myself that year that I would spend my holidays from school back home at the Grove. On the fifth of July, Christy accompanied Mollie and myself to the railway station. We bade each other adieu and I embarked on my journey home. Mollie sat herself at my feet and promptly fell asleep. The train trip gave me a much needed time to think.

The journey itself was almost symbolic as it brought me from one world to another world. Why! In Dublin I was exposed constantly to reminders of its poverty. There too, I was utterly independent and never felt the need to explain myself, nor my position, to anyone. After all I was employed in a most ordinary National School in the town itself.

In Dublin too, I had found myself very much involved in Ireland's struggle for independence from the British Empire. As I travelled home to the Grove that day I pondered my commitment to it. Had I become too involved in it, and had I taken a thorny road? Would life have been less complex for me had I taken Georgina's route and married a man of high social standing?

I thought too about Christy. There was no doubt that the two of us were committed to the same Cause. We were extremely comfortable in each other's company but I lacked any very passionate feeling towards him and I never envisaged marriage to him.

I thought too of my very privileged up-bringing at the Grove which was followed by my elite education in boarding school. I also thought about how I had found myself identifying with the ordinary people with whom I felt so at ease unlike the some of the snobs I had encountered in my young life. Indeed, I even met a few of them at boarding school.

Odd as it may seem, it was my school outing to Henrietta Street all those years ago with Miss Hunt that had made a profound impact on me. I had seen first hand, poverty the like of which I had never witnessed prior to then. The tenants on Papa's estate were wealthy compared to the poverty stricken people of that street. If there was a God, surely we were all part of his creation and, thus, the onus was on the privileged people to care for the vulnerable? I was lost in thought for such a while that the rail journey had ended before I realised it.

Papa was there at the railway station to greet myself and Mollie. I was so, so happy to see him. He gave me that lovely warm smile which had a certain reassurance about it — a reassurance that I certainly needed at that time, for, in truth, I was a little frightened and I needed the security of home and Papa.

Papa parked the motor car in front of the Grove itself and I remember alighting from it with Mollie in toe. Why! Duckworth Grove itself stood there as solid as ever, impervious to change. It reminded me of a sentry on duty, guarding the landscape of the surrounding County.

I was so happy to see Ellie as she too represented solidity and consistency. However, time had marched on and I had never noticed until then how poor Ellie had aged a lot. Her hair was totally grey and she required a walking-stick. She had officially retired and was living as she always did in the servants' quarters. I rarely ventured there. However, that day I accompanied her back to her quarters. I have to say I was rather shocked and I became quite emotional when I looked about her little home. She had newspaper cuttings with pictures of William, my brother, plus all sorts of mementos of his life on her living room wall. I never doubted her devotion to our family. However, that particular day I thought to myself how wrong it all was that Ellie had in effect subjugated her own dreams and ambitions to the service of our family. As Mildred often said 'We are all equal in the eyes of God' yet it was quite clear to me that, in reality, this was not the case.

We, the Duckworth Family, were as powerful in ways as any of the powerful business people in Dublin Town and, as such, had a moral responsibility to ensure that fairness and kindness were evident at all times. Papa unlike some other landlords respected and appreciated his tenants for their contribution to the smooth operation of our Estate.

Papa was far from oblivious to the revolution that had already taken place regarding the changes in land ownership and it did not seem to perturb him to any great measure. He was quite happy to spend much of his time grafting rose trees and studying various botanical aspects to the gardens of the Grove. I often both heard and saw Papa deeply engaged in conversation about the merits of growing slug resistant plants with our head gardener, Tom.

I thoroughly enjoyed the Summer of 1910 at home at the Grove, although nothing remarkable happened during my time there. Suffice to say I was content to wander about the estate with Mollie in toe and to observe the activities taking place on the land. I thought to myself how lovely it was to see the fields of golden young corn and if, I was lucky, to spot an occasional corncrake.

Other days, I made a trip into the village of Alm and went to Wynn's little hotel for afternoon tea. More often than not such times brought me back to the halcyon days that I had spent there with Danial. Beautiful memories from another time. A time when I was young, carefree and very much in love with Danial.

That Summer of 1910 was all too short at home at the Grove. In truth, I had not missed Christy or any of the other people I knew in Dublin to any great extent. It had almost been a relief to have had a respite from all the turmoil of change that was happening in the capital itself. Both Christy and I were heavily involved in that melting pot of change there and I wondered at the time what the eventual outcome would be.

War clouds had gathered between the major powers of Great Britain and Europe, over the crisis in the Balkans. The question of Home Rule for Ireland was on the cards at Westminster. Many people in Ireland felt that it was only a matter of time until Home Rule would be granted to Ireland. However, that was not what was needed, much less wanted by my friends and, indeed, my acquaintances. In common with them, I felt that Ireland's independence had to be an independence gained on our terms, not those of limited 'freedom' acquiesced to by British parliamentary laws.

On the 24th of August I bade Papa farewell at Dromod railway station and travelled to Dublin with Mollie.

Chapter 8

I remember well staring out the window as the train reached Broadstone railway station on that stifling hot August afternoon. Christy was standing at the edge of the platform and he looked most handsome, with his usual tossed hair and his shirt sleeves rolled up to reveal his strong tanned arms. I thought to myself how attractive he looked.

We embraced and, as we did, he said 'Ettie, would you ever think of marrying me?' I was totally taken aback and I stood there in shock and, to add to my confused state, Mollie was barking and jumping in all directions. It was obvious that she was clearly delighted to see Christy. All I can remember replying was 'Give me time. Give me time!' It may have been a coward's reply but, in truth, I was happy with the way things were and I had no wish or desire to change my living situation. Christy never mentioned it again, much to my relief.

Christy was more committed than ever to Ireland's independence from Britain, coupled with his passionate interest in James Larkin's newly founded Irish Transport and General Workers Union. Indeed, around that time too, he met James Connolly and was absolutely enthralled by Connolly's vision for the working-class woman or man. However, Christy's employer at the printing works was becoming increasingly outraged at his Trade Union membership and, less than two years later, he found himself along with many other employees being locked out out of their jobs for possessing union membership and striking. It was an appalling situation. Many of the poorest unskilled workers in Dublin who had gone on strike found themselves in a desperate situation. Christy's poor father was among those unfortunate people.

Needless to say, it affected me greatly, too. Many of those on strike had children attending our school and, daily, I encountered their lean and hungry little faces in the classroom. I did my best and I became a familiar sight pedaling my boneshaker along the Liffey quays weighed down with parcels of food from the kitchen in

Radharc na Life, which I then distributed among my class.

There was so much happening so, so rapidly. Europe was on the brink of war, the Home Rule Bill was at its Third Stage in Westminster and the *Irish Volunteers* were formed. Both Christy and Pádraig attended its inaugural meeting in the Rotunda Room on the 25th of November 1913. In the words of P. H. Pearse, 'Ireland armed would be able to make a better bargain with the Empire than Ireland unarmed'.

Both Bessie and I had been members of Inighinidhe na hÉireann so it was almost a natural progression for us to join *Cumann na mBan*, the women's equivalent of the *Irish Volunteers,* which was led by Agnes O' Farrelly, Mary Mac Swiney and Countess Markievicz.

I became a regular spectator on Aston Quay as I watched Christy and the other Volunteers march under the noses of the Dublin Metropolitan Police, along Batchelor's Walk. They marched along the Liffey quays in full Irish

Volunteer uniform with their camáns on their shoulders.

Almost at the same time in Europe on the 28th of June 1914 Archduke Ferdinand, Heir to the Austro-Hungarian Empire was assassinated in Sarajevo. It was the spark that ignited the Great War. On the 28th of July, Austria declared war on Serbia. On the 1st of August, Germany declared war on Russia. Less than three days later Germany declared war on France and invaded Belgium.

Asquith and the Westminster Government gave Germany an ultimatum to withdraw from Belgium by mid-night on the 2nd of August. The ultimatum was ignored by the German powers and, on the 4th of August, Great Britain declared war on Germany. Great Britain had gone to war 'to protect the rights of small nations'. I remember laughing to myself at the time and thinking what kind of a mind-set prevailed in Westminster? How could they possibly apply that thinking regarding Belgium and totally dismiss that justice to Ireland?

The powers of Europe were truly at war. The Home Rule Bill was shelved and the threat of conscription to the British Army hung over Ireland. It was a very strange time and although I was a very active member of Cumann na mBan, I had not held a gun, much less knew how to use one. That was to change. Why! On Saint Patrick's Day 1916, Christy handed me a Mauser pistol and he told me I would need it very soon. I stared at it like a mystified child. When eventually I became comfortable holding it, Christy and I did target practice at a safe distance from *Radharc na Life*. Poor Mollie yelped and took cover under a bush every time I fired the pistol. Much to my own amazement, within a relatively short time, I was able to load, aim and fire the pistol as well as any of the men in the Volunteers. Possessing such an ability made me uncomfortable and the nearer the time came to use it for its intended purpose the more uncomfortable I became.

Christy called to *Radrarc na Life* very early on the morning of the 23rd of April 1916 prior to attend a meeting called for by the Supreme

Council of the IRB. I left the house a little later and attended Easter Sunday Service at Christ Church. My heart was heavy as I thought about the loaded pistol in the drawer beside my bed.

After Service I returned to *Radharc na Life*. The house was empty as it was the day off for Mary and John. I went to my bedroom drawer and took out the pistol. I unloaded it and wrapped it carefully in my neckerchief. I then packed it and a few personal belongings into a bag and called Mollie. Resolutely, I closed the hall door and walked with Mollie out on to Parkgate Street, down by the Liffey quays in the direction of the Ha'penny Bridge. I stood on the bridge with Mollie by my side. I threw the pistol into the flowing river, watched it splash into the water and stared as it as it sank to the river bed. All the while, darling Mama's words resonated through my mind 'Ettie always be gentle, always be kind'.

Epilogue - The Palmerstown Papers

In 2009, Waterstown Park was officially opened. This beautiful parkland is located along the banks of the River Liffey in Palmerstown. However, prior to its current usage as an amenity area it was used as a dump up to the early 1980s. In spite of that, it still attracted people who wished to walk by the river-bank. Éamonn and his wife, Trása frequently traversed it with their dogs.

On the 26th of May 1979, whilst Éamonn and Trása were walking that way, they spotted a rusty tin box, which contained a bundle of papers of some sort, lying on the ground. Curiosity got the better of Éamonn and he decided to investigate. To their sheer amazement, they had come upon part of a memoir read-written by a lady by the name of the name Henrietta Duckworth.

To this day, it remains a mystery as the remainder of Henrietta's memoirs have yet to be found.